Shark's Tooth

cola Moon

strated by Robert McPhillips

OXFORD
UNIVERSITY PRESS

Deep down in the sea there was
an old wreck.

Shark lived in the old wreck.

One day Shark was feeling sad.

"My tooth hurts," said Shark.

"Let me see," said Octopus.

Octopus looked in Shark's mouth.

"I can help you," he said.

Octopus pulled Shark's tooth.

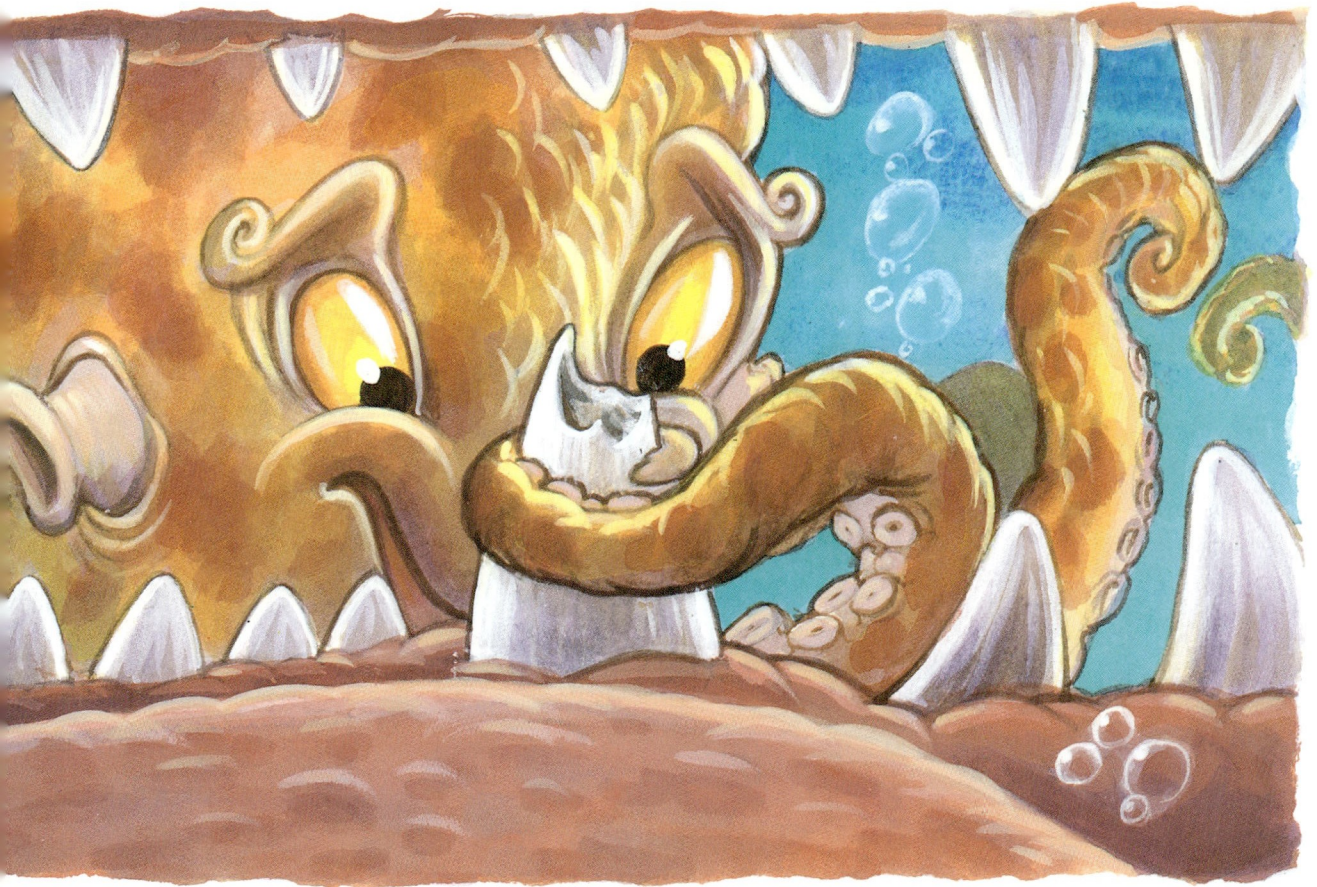

He pulled the tooth with two legs
but it wouldn't come out.

e pulled the tooth with four legs
it it wouldn't come out.

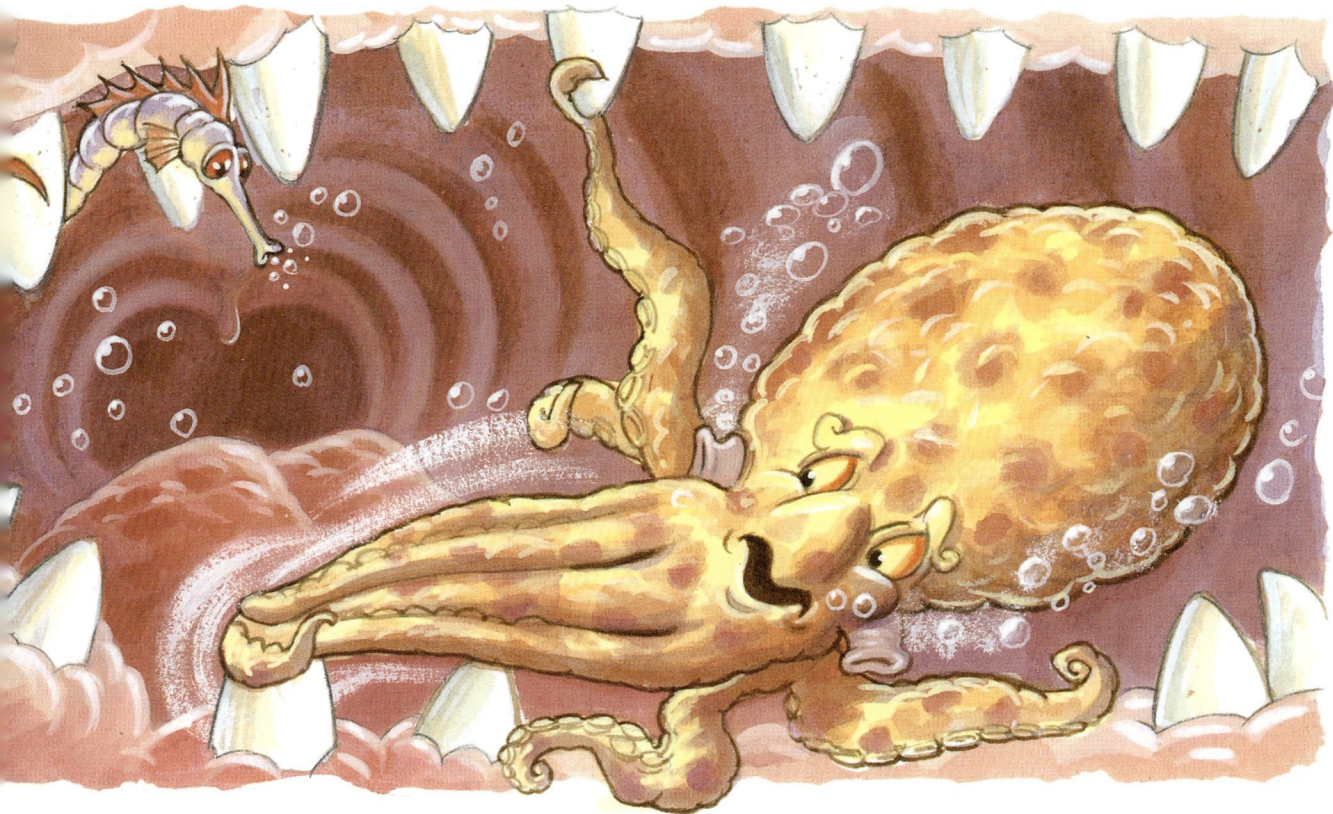

He pulled the tooth with six legs
but it wouldn't come out.

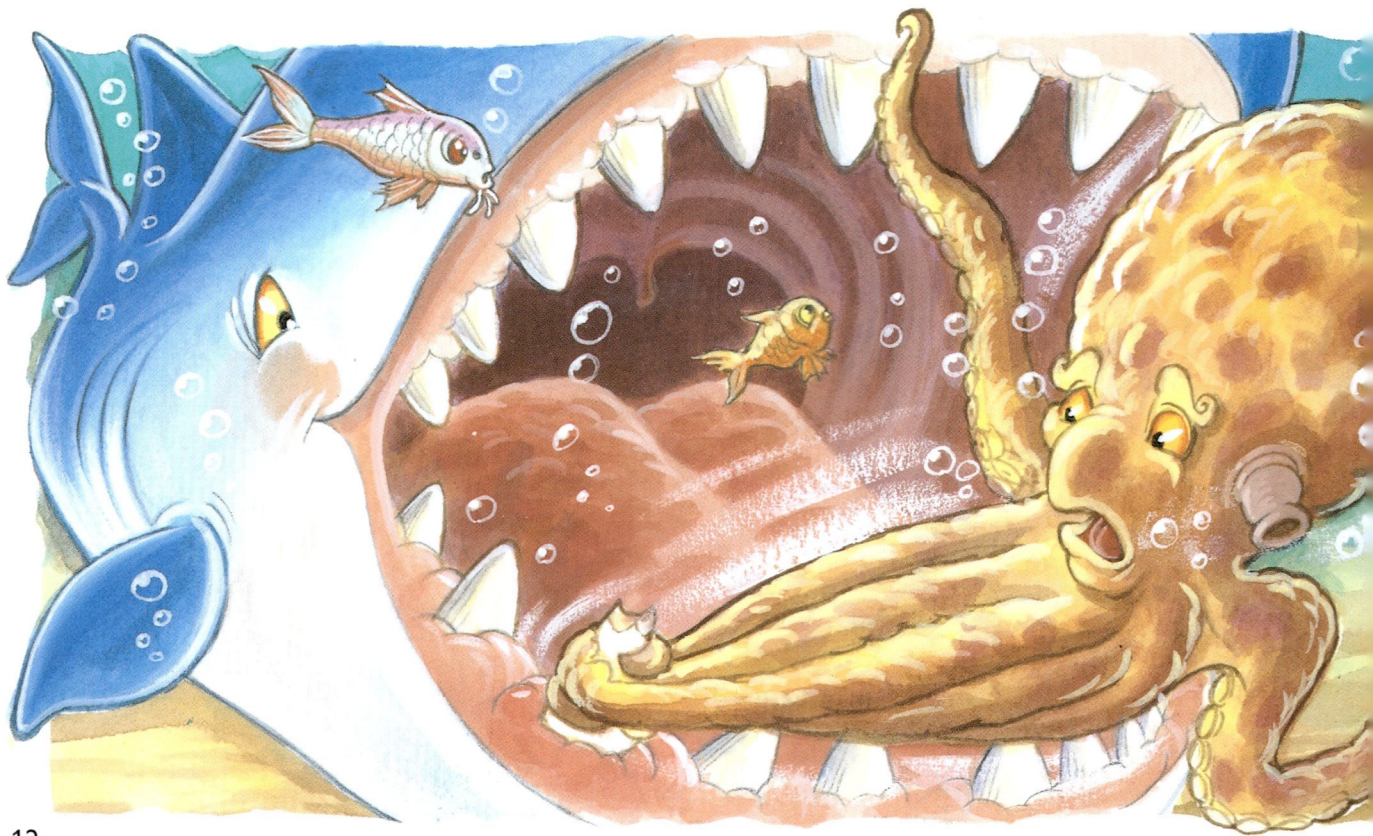

He pulled the tooth with all his legs.

POP! Shark's tooth came out.

"I feel better now," said Shark.

"I don't," said Octopus.
"My legs hurt!"